When Katie's Mum and Dad Separated

by **Sarah, Duchess of York**
Illustrated by Ian Cunliffe

When Katie's Mum and Dad Separated

helping hand books

First published in Great Britain 2007 by Lloyds Pharmacy Ltd
Sapphire Court, Walsgrave Triangle, Coventry CV2 2TX
www.lloydspharmacy.com

In consultation with Cameron Wilson Ltd

Illustrated by Ian Cunliffe

'Ten Helpful Hints' contributed by Dr. Richard Woolfson,
child psychologist, Fellow of the British Psychological Society.

Printed in China

British Library Cataloguing in Publication Data
A catalogue record for this book is available from the British Library

ISBN 978-1-906260-04-0

All children face many new experiences as they grow up and helping them to understand and deal with each is one of the most demanding and rewarding things we do as parents. The helping hand books are for both children and parents to read, perhaps together. Each simple story describes a childhood experience and shows some of the ways in which to make it a positive one. I do hope these books encourage children and parents to talk about these sometimes difficult issues; talking together goes a long way to finding a solution.

Sarah,

Sarah, Duchess of York

The first thing in the morning was the worst time.

Katie would wake up with an empty feeling and then she would remember.

Dad was no longer living with them.

It had been a few months before when Mum and Dad had sat her down and told her that Dad was going to live somewhere else, as they did not want to be together any longer and that, although they did not love each other in the same way any more, they both loved her very much.

Katie's first thought had been that she would not see her Dad anymore but Dad had told her that she would be with him every other weekend and longer in the holidays and that they would do lots of things together.

Katie thought back to what had happened since that day.

She and Mum had moved from their house into a flat about five miles away.

At first, Katie had not wanted to move at all but now she liked her new home.

She loved her new bedroom, was surrounded by all her favourite things and, most importantly, had made two good friends who lived in the same street: David and Megan.

Her Mum worked very hard so Katie tried to help her as much as she could to look after the flat and her Mum called her 'Head of Housekeeping', which made Katie feel very important!

She loved the way her Mum now smiled a lot more and there was none of the arguing that had gone on when Mum and Dad were together.

The weekends with her Dad were good too, she soon got used to his cooking and her bunk bed.

Her Dad always organised something that would be fun, whether it was a walk to the park to feed the ducks or a trip to the cinema.

Katie loved going to the cinema and if she could persuade her Dad to buy her popcorn, that was even better!

"So stop feeling sorry for yourself," Katie told herself crossly one day as she got out of bed and went down to breakfast.

"I've got good news!" said her Mum excitedly,

"We can have Aunty Masie's cottage in Devon while she is away for a week in August.

It is near the coast, and the best bit is that there's room for three, so you can bring Megan or perhaps Grace from school."

Katie was thrilled but thoughtful.

"Megan is my best friend so it should be her but she's not very good at swimming. Grace loves swimming but I don't want to upset Megan by not inviting her. It's a problem."

"It's a nice problem to have!" said her Mum.

The next weekend Katie went to her Dad.

As they were walking through the park, her Dad said, "It's time we thought about a summer holiday, you and me. I've been doing a bit of investigating and I think it would be fun to go camping in France."

"In a tent?" asked Katie.

"That's usually what camping involves!" smiled her Dad.

"In France?"

"Yes, I don't think there are too many lions and tigers there!" laughed her Dad,

"So we shall be quite safe."

"Can I bring a friend?" asked Katie.

"No, it will just be the two of us." replied Dad.

"But Mum is letting me bring a friend with me on our holiday," Katie complained.

"Then you're a very lucky girl, after all you are having two holidays, so I don't want to hear more about it," said her Dad firmly.

That evening, Katie was sitting at home back with her Mum, having tea.

"Mum," she said thoughtfully,

"why can't we all go on holiday together?

Is it because of me?"

Her Mum sighed, "Of course not. It's just that your Dad and I find it easier to live apart rather than together. It's something we've both thought about for a long time and it's not going to change. But we both want to be with you so you're going to have a busy summer!"

Katie lay in bed thinking about the weekend. It always upset her a bit when she left her Mum to be with her Dad. And then again, she was sad to leave her Dad when she came back to her Mum.

But she saw that both her Mum and Dad seemed happier with their new lives and perhaps in time she too would stop worrying about what she missed from her old life as she started to enjoy things about her new life.

She soon fell asleep and had the strangest dream. She was on holiday in a cottage in France. In the garden was a tent where the friendliest lions and tigers used to sleep. And the strangest thing of all was that they could speak – in French of course!

The helping hand books

Lloydspharmacy